Gout Hater's Cookbook I

Recipes
lower in purines

and
lower in fat
by Jodi Schneiter

4th Edition, Revised

Gout Hater's Cookbook I
The Low Purine Diet Cookbook

Published by:
> Southeast Media Productions
> 87 Piedmont Drive
> Palm Coast, Florida 32164
> USA
> Phone: 386.206.1163
> Fax: 386.586.5564
> Website: www.gout-haters.com

Library of Congress Control Number: 2004095427

ISBN-10: 1-888141-74-3
ISBN-13: 978-1-888141-74-0

Please note: The contents of this book are in no way intended for use as a substitute for medical advice. Always consult your physician before making any changes in your diet. The information provided may vary from the regimen given to your by your physician or dietitian. As every individual case is different, please follow your recommended regimen, including diet and medications.

Many thanks to the Purine Research Society
and its efforts to help children with purine autism.

Special thanks to Dr. Robert C. Bennett
for his creative gourmet contributions.

Contents

A Little About
Gout Hater's Cookbook I

Attacks of gout have often been characterized as the king's proverbial swollen big toe.

Indeed, gout was traditionally thought to be caused by an intake of too many rich foods.

Actually, gout is typically brought on by the body's inability to eliminate excess uric acid, a by-product of purines.

Attacks can be brought on by obesity, alcohol binges, use of low-dose aspirin, diuretic medication, hypertension or an extreme change in diet. Attacks can also be triggered by trauma or surgery.

About 5.9 million people in the United States suffer from gout. Its occurrence is seen more in men than women. Most cases involve men over 40. Cases involving women are usually seen after menopause. Aside from being extremely painful, gout can be an indicator of other serious illnesses.

Gout can be treated using several methods. These include symptom-relieving medicines, preventive medicines, limiting alcohol consumption, and a diet of low-purine foods.

When you begin to control your diet with healthier eating, you are not only helping your body to fight future attacks of gout, you are helping to fight other health problems as well.

The recipes in *Gout Hater's Cookbook* avoid foods that are high in purines. They are designed to help you on your way to lowering uric acid levels by healthy, delicious eating.

Please note that fats are not considered high in purines. On the other hand, a large intake of fat is not in your best health interests. Because of this, the recipes will also minimize the use of saturated fat.

Remember that moderation is the key. In fact, the severity of a gout attack can be worsened by certain changes in diet. Your physician might suggest that you do not change any of your eating or drinking habits until the attack of gout has subsided.

It cannot be stressed enough that any diet should be approved by your physician.

Once you begin to come up with recipes on your own, you will be pleasantly surprised by all of the gourmet dishes you can create.

In addition, please note that the lists of highest, moderately high and lower purine foods contained in this book may vary from the list supplied by your own physician.

This book is not intended as a substitute for the advice given by your physician. Please be sure to follow the instructions of your physician or dietitian.

FOODS ALLOWED
GREEN LIGHT
(LOWEST LEVEL PURINES)

Beets (except beet tops), broccoli, carrots, celery, coconuts, corn, cucumbers, fruits, berries and fruit juice, eggplant, green string beans (not bulging), grits, hominy, jicama, leafy greens (except those listed in moderate level group), leeks, lettuce, okra, olives, onions, parsnips, peppers, potatoes, radishes, rhubarb, sago, squash, tomatoes, turnips, vegetable soups (not containing meat stock or meat extracts. Those containing high-purine vegetables should be in moderation), water chestnuts.

Nuts (except peanuts, which should be in moderation - see Legumes, page 104)

Dairy (low fat or fat free): cottage cheese, cheese, eggs (no more than one yolk per day; more than one white is allowed), ice cream, margarine, milk, ricotta, yogurt. Watch the ingredients for xanthan/xanthum gum or xanthine.

Cereals (except whole grain), corn flakes, semolina pasta/macaroni (preferable 100% semolina), white rice, tapioca.

White flour (without malted barley flour added), matzoh, white rice flour, arrowroot flour, baker's yeast (only as a part of baking. Yeast supplements not allowed), white bread, French bread, plain white bagels (watch for malt), white pita bread.

Ketchup, mustard, mayonnaise, honey, sugar

De-caf coffee, tea, sodas: non-cola, non-caffeine

Vegetable oils: Canola, olive, soy

Foods Allowed
Yellow Light
(Moderate Level Purines)

The following non-meat items are allowed, but are grouped differently here only because they contain higher purine levels. According to a 12 year study published in the *New England Journal of Medicine* (see page 8), a moderate amount of vegetables rich in purines did not increase the risk of gout.

Artichokes, asparagus, beans, bean sprouts, beet tops, bok choy, Brussels sprouts, cabbage, cauliflower, coconuts, dried beans and peas, kale, legumes (page 104), lentils, mushrooms, peanuts and peanut butter, peanut oil, peas, soy/soy products (including tofu, soy sauce and soy flour), spinach, Swiss chard

Wheat germ and whole grain cereal or flour, including barley, barley malt, bran, brown rice, oatmeal, oats, rye, pumpernickel, graham flour, malt, whole wheat, whole wheat flour; macaroni products not labeled as semolina or semolina durum.

Your system may be able to tolerate 3 ounces (about the size of a deck of playing cards) of the following foods per day. (Please check with your physician or dietitian.

Skinless white meat chicken or turkey.

Beef: Your prescribed diet may also allow small servings of beef (included in Foods Not Allowed, below). Therefore , a small number of recipes (that contain reduced serving sizes of meat) have been provided.

Foods and Ingredients Not Allowed
Red Light
(Avoid These Items)

The following foods and ingedients are either very high in purines or otherwise not allowed in the restricted purine diet (See Important Research Results, page 8):

Alcohol, coffee, tea, chocolate, cocoa, cola drinks, carob, carob bean gum, caffeine.

All types of seafood, especially anchovies, caviar, fish roe, herring, ocean perch, sardines, scallops, smelt, sprat, trout and tuna.

Brains, game meats, horse, kidney, lamb, meat extracts/stock, organ meats, sausage, soups made from meat stock or extracts, spleen, tongue.

Brewer's yeast, yeast supplements, MSG, xanthine/xanthan gum, lard, powdered or evaporated milk, whole milk/milk products.

Important Research Results

According to a twelve year study published in March of 2004 in the New England Journal of Medicine, it is no longer necessary to avoid vegetables that are high in purines. The study stated that there was no association found between an intake of vegetables high in purines and an increase in the risk of gout. However, it did mention in conclusion that purine-rich vegetables could be eaten in moderation, and apparently not in unlimited amounts.

As reported in the same study, the daily intake of low-fat milk and yogurt showed a marked decrease in the risk of attacks. The largest decrease was seen in those who drank at least 2 glasses of milk each day. Interestingly, this finding corresponds with other reports which showed an increase in uric acid levels due to an abstinence from dairy products.

In contrast, each additional serving per day of meats relatively high in purines increased the risk of gout by 21%, and each additional serving of seafood each week increased the risk by 7%!!

In addition, men with a higher body mass carried an increased risk, and alcohol consumption posed an increased risk.

Additional Notes

--A daily intake of at least 1/2 pound of cherries has been said to help reduce uric acid levels in some cases.

-- Notice that sugar and fats have been listed as foods that are lower in purines. Although they are on the "foods allowed" list, they still contribute to obesity and ill health, and therefore should be consumed with care and moderation.

--About one third of the uric acid normally produced in the body comes from food, with the remainder being produced through regular metabolism.

--Increased daily water intake is important. Dehydration can provoke attacks of gout. Try to drink six to eight glasses of water per day. This will help in both diluting the uric acid and in flushing it out of your system.

--An intake of 500 mg of vitamin C can help reduce uric acid levels

--Crash diets can elevate the degree of hyperurecemia. Changes in diet should be gradual.

--Remember that moderation is the key, and when gout can be an indicator of other serious problems, any foods that contribute to ill health should be avoided.

--Always consult your physician before making any changes in your diet or eating habits.

Appetizers
and
Beverages

Lemon Ginger Tea

1 quart water
3 tsp lemon juice
1-inch chunk cut from a ginger root

Preparation:
    Bring water and lemon juice to a boil in a large saucepan. While water is heating, peel and chop ginger root. Place ginger in tea ball and add to boiling water.
    Continue to boil 1 minute. Cover and steep 5-7 minutes. Remove tea ball and pour into teapot. Sweeten with honey or sweetener as desired.
    Serves four.

Evening Tea

4 tea bags of chamomile tea
1 tea bag of peppermint tea
1-1/2 quarts of water

Preparation:
    Heat water to boiling, add tea bags and steep for about 5 minutes. Serve hot. If desired, add 1/2 packet of artificial sweetener to each cup.
Makes 1 1/2 quarts.

Olive Spread

8 oz. package cream cheese (no xanthan gum)
1/2 cup chopped olives

Preparation:

Empty container of cream cheese into a medium mixing bowl. Add olives.

Blend with electric hand mixer until ingredients are thoroughly combined.

Serve spread over bagels or french bread.

Spiced Tea

1 quart water
1 family size (or 3 regular size) bag de-caf tea
3 cinnamon sticks
4 whole cloves
1 cup cherry juice
1 cup apple juice

Preparation:

Combine ingredients in large saucepan. Bring to a soft boil. Reduce heat and simmer for about 10 minutes. Remove cloves, cinnamon sticks and tea bag. Serve hot or chilled.

Makes 1 1/2 quarts.

Orange Punch

1 can frozen orange juice
1 quart club soda (or sparkling water)
1 cup ice
1 orange

Preparation:

    Cut orange into thin slices and set aside.

    Combine club soda and frozen orange juice in a 2-quart pitcher.

    Stir lightly until well combined.

    Add ice and serve in glasses garnished with orange slices.

    Makes about 1-1/2 quarts.

Apple-Cherry Tea

1 cup cherry juice
2 cups apple juice
2 cups water
3 cinnamon sticks
4 whole cloves

Preparation:
Combine ingredients in saucepan and bring to a boil. Immediately lower heat and simmer for about 10 minutes. Remove cinnamon and cloves. Serve hot, warm or chilled.
Makes about 1 quart.

Lemonade

Juice from 5 lemons or limes
1-1/4 cups sugar
water

Preparation:
Combine juice and sugar. Add water to make 2 quarts and stir until sugar is dissolved.
Serve chilled.

Lemon Grass Tea

1 bunch of lemon grass
3 - 1/2" chunks of ginger
1 gallon water
honey

Preparation:

Thoroughly wash lemon grass. Tie into one large slip knot. This will make the grass easier to remove once the tea is made.

Place water in large pot. Add lemon grass and ginger. Bring to a boil. Continue boiling for about 5-10 minutes. There will be a wonderful lemon aroma in your kitchen. Serve with honey.

Cherry Freeze

2 cups cherry juice
2 cups ice

Preparation:

Combine ingredients in electric blender and blend until smooth. Serve with straws. Serves four.

Variation: Wild cherry: Add 3 tsp lemon juice, and 2 tbsp sugar. (adjust to taste as desired).

French Onion Soup

3 large onions
5 cups water
2 tsp margarine
2 tsp flour
4 slices reduced fat provolone cheese
4 slices hard french bread
1/2 tsp garlic powder
1/8 tsp pepper

Preparation:

Chop, but do not mince, onions. Saute in 2/3 cup water until water is reduced. Continue to saute, adding margarine and flour.

Stir constantly, cooking until onions are glazed.

Immediately add remainder of water, garlic powder and pepper. Bring to a boil, then cover and reduce heat to low. Simmer for about 35 minutes.

While soup is cooking, trim bread slices to fit into each of four microwaveable bowls. Pour soup into. Top each with bread, then cheese.

Place each bowl into microwave for about 20 seconds to melt cheese. Serve immediately.

Serves four.

Potato Soup

5 medium potatoes
1 medium onion, minced
1/2 tsp salt
1/2 tsp garlic powder
1 cup skim milk
2 tsp flour
2 quarts water

Preparation:

Bring water to boil in a large cooking pot. Add salt and garlic powder. While water is heating, peel potatoes and cut into small, bite-sized pieces.

Rinse and add, with onions, to boiling water. Return to a boil, then lower heat to medium low, allowing soup to simmer for about 40 minutes or until potatoes are tender.

In a separate bowl, combine flour and milk. Blend thoroughly with a fork. Stir milk mixture into potatoes. Cook, stirring often but gently, until soup reaches desired consistency. Serve hot.

Serves six.

Quick Snack

Something on a cracker: Spread veggie-flavored fat-free cream cheese (check for spinach!) over crackers. A delicious, albeit simple, appetizer.

Herb Butter

2 tbsp finely chopped fresh parsley
1 tsp dried tarragon
1/2 tsp onion powder
1/8 tsp garlic powder
3/4 cup margarine, softened
1/2 Tbsp lemon juice
salt
pepper
nutmeg

Preparation:

In a medium mixing bowl, combine margarine, parsley, tarragon, onion powder and garlic powder. Blend with electric mixer until creamy.

Add lemon juice and a pinch of nutmeg. Blend in a small amount of salt and pepper to taste.

Place into butter molds or small air-tight container and chill. This can be served as an appetizer dip or spread over crackers.

Variation: replace margarine with fat-free cream cheese

Stuffed Jalapenos

18 fresh jalapenos
1 small package of cornbread stuffing mix
5 egg whites
1/4 cup skim milk
1 small onion
1/2 cup water
2 cloves garlic

Preparation:

Cut jalapenos in half lengthwise and remove seeds. Lay out in rows on cookie sheet(s). Set aside.

Cook one half of egg whites in a non-stick skillet and set aside to cool.

Mince onion and saute in water until transparent. Set aside.

Prepare stuffing according to directions on package. Place in mixing bowl.

Add onion, remaining egg whites, milk and garlic.

Chop cooked eggs and add to mixture. Mix by hand until all ingredients are thoroughly combined. Spoon mixture into jalapeno halves.

Bake in a 375 degree oven for about 30 minutes or until stuffing tops are browned and jalapenos have become slightly tender.

Cool for 10 minutes and serve.

Makes about 3 dozen.

Stuffed Jalapenos II

1 dozen fresh jalapenos
1 tbsp dried minced onion
1 tbsp dried minced garlic
1 cup reduced fat grated cheddar cheese
1 cup herb flavored stuffing
3/4 cup water

Preparation:

Slice jalapenos lengthwise and remove seeds. Set aside. Heat water to boiling and add to herb stuffing. Add remainder of ingredients, mixing with spoon until thoroughly combined.

Fill jalapenos with stuffing mixture and bake at 350 for about 35 minutes or until browned. Cool and serve.

Makes two dozen.

Pimiento Cheese Dip

1 1/2 cups prepared pimiento cheese spread
1 cup pitted green olives
pepper

Preparation:

Mince olives in blender. Add pimiento cheese and a pinch of pepper. Blend again, but only long enough for ingredients to become evenly combined.

Chill and serve.

Deviled Eggs

one dozen eggs
egg substitute equal to 6 eggs
1/3 cup vanilla yogurt
paprika
1 tsp pepper

Preparation:

Cook egg substitute in a non-stick skillet until fully done. Set aside.

Boil eggs in salted water for about 30 minutes. Drain water from pan and immediately cover eggs with cold water to help the shells come off easily.

Remove and discard the shells. With a sharp knife, cut eggs in half lengthwise. Remove yolks and discard.

Rinse any remaining yolk from the egg whites and tap dry with a paper towel.

Because the stuffing will go back into the egg white halves, you will want to be sure that they look perfect. Therefore, all egg whites that are broken or will not look good on the serving plate should be either discarded or finely chopped and added to the stuffing.

Place any chopped egg whites into a mixing bowl. Chop cooked egg substitute and add to bowl. Add pepper and mayonnaise. Mix well either with a spoon or with a blender on low speed, until all lumps are gone and mixture is smooth.

Spoon mixture into egg white halves, filling both the yolk area and over the top.

Smooth a little with spoon to make the eggs appear to be half white, half stuffing.

Sprinkle with paprika. Arrange eggs in a geometric pattern on a serving dish.

Makes up to 2 dozen.

Vegetable Soup

1 onion
3 quarts water
2 small cans tomato paste
4 cloves garlic
1/8 tsp salt
1/8 tsp pepper
1 pound carrots
2 medium-large potatoes

Preparation:

Place water in cooking pot on stove. Bring to a boil. While water is coming to a boil, chop onion and add to pot. Add tomato paste, salt and pepper. Mince garlic and add to pot. Wash, peel and cut carrots into bite-sized pieces. Add to pot. Cut potatoes into pieces and add.

Once the mixture again comes to a boil, reduce heat and simmer, stirring occasionally, for about 1 hour or until potatoes and carrots are fully cooked.

Serves eight.

Garlic Bread

bottled minced garlic
margarine
sliced white or Italian bread
dried chopped parsley

Preparation:

Spread a thin layer of margarine over each bread slice. Top with a generous layer of minced garlic and sprinkle with parsley.

Grease a cookie sheet with non-stick cooking spray. Place bread on cookie sheet and broil in oven for about 10 minutes or until garlic begins to brown.

Quick Snack

Cheese Bread: Toast a piece of bread, as usual, in your toaster. Place toast on a dish and top with sliced cheese and oregano. Heat in microwave until cheese melts (about 20 seconds).

Fancy Pecans

one 10-oz. package of shelled pecans
3 tbsp steak sauce (no xanthan gum)
3 tbsp water
1/4 tsp garlic powder
1/4 tsp onion powder

Preparation:

Combine steak sauce, water, garlic powder and onion powder in large skillet or sauce pan. Stir ingredients until blended.

Add pecans and cook on medium high, stirring occasionally, until all liquid is absorbed. Cool and serve warm.

Serves about 6.

Xanthine - Why?

Xanthine appears in a final stage of the metabolism of purines into uric acid. Coffee, tea, spinach, chocolate and cola drinks all contain caffeine or similar substances called methylxanthines. When checking ingredients: beware of xanthine, xanthan gum, or nonspecific vegetable gums, which appear often in dairy products.

Beet Salad

4 beets
1/2 medium onion
1/4 cup apple cider vinegar
1/2 cup canola oil
1/2 tsp garlic powder
1/8 tsp pepper
1/4 tsp oregano

Preparation:

Peel and slice beets. Cook in boiling water until tender. Chill. Set aside.

Finely chop onion. Place in mixing bowl. Add remaining ingredients. Mix until blended. Pour over beets. Fold until beets are evenly coated. Allow to marinate 10-15 minutes. Fold again before serving.

Serves four.

Melon Salad

1 medium watermelon half
1 canteloupe
1 honeydew melon
4 red delicious apples
1/3 cup orange juice

Preparation:

Hollow out meat from watermelon half and cut into bite-sized pieces. Set aside hollowed half.

Place pieces into large bowl. Peel and remove seeds from canteloupe and melon. Cut into bite-sized pieces and add to bowl. Set aside.

Core apples, leaving peel on, and cut into bite-sized pieces. Place in small mixing bowl.

Add orange juice and mix gently until orange juice coats apple pieces completely (this will help keep apple pieces from turning brown).

Add to melon mixture, and gently fold until orange juice is well distributed. Spoon into hollowed watermelon half. Serve immediately or cover with plastic wrap and refrigerate.

Serves about twelve.

Orange and Raisin Salad

1/2 cup raisins
4 navel oranges
1/4 cup french dressing (see page 77)
1/4 cup plain nonfat yogurt (no xanthan gum)

Preparation:

Steam raisins in a small amount of water, in a covered pan, for about 10 minutes. Allow to cool. Place in mixing bowl. Peel oranges and separate slices. Cut slices in half and add to raisins. Add yogurt and dressing. Mix well until thoroughly combined. Chill.

Serves four.

Mexican Rice Cooler

3 cups water
1/2 cup rice
5 cups iced water
2 cinnamon sticks
1/2 tsp vanilla
1/2 cup sugar

Preparation:

In a medium saucepan, bring 3 cups water to a full boil. Add rice and cinnamon sticks. Continue boiling for about 4 minutes. Add vanilla and boil 1 more minute. Remove from heat. Add to 5 cups iced water. Chill overnight.

Before serving, carefully pour off liquid into a 2-quart pitcher. Add sugar, stir and serve.

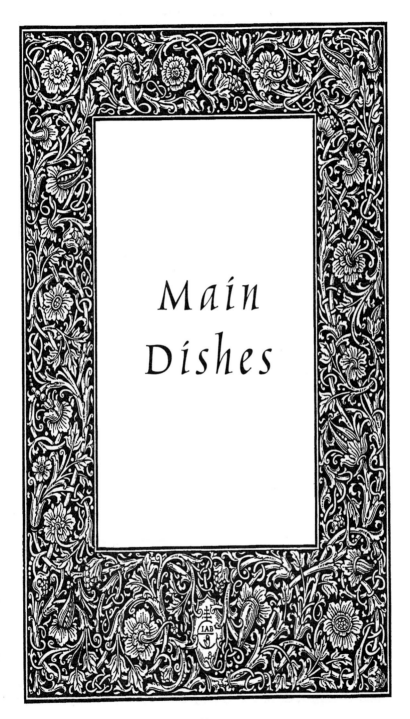

Main Dishes

Try to begin with as many raw ingredients as possible, beginning with fresh foods when you can, rather than frozen or canned.

Always check the ingredients on any product you are about to purchase! Avoid soy, MSG and xanthan gum. (See MSG, Appendix, pg. 104)

Don't add sauces or gravies that are meat-based; and when cooking pasta, use 100% semolina or durum semolina.

If you are going to eat a dish that contains a food higher in purines, make sure that the amount of purines is reduced by adding other savory dishes or ingredients that are low in purines. Meat can also be boiled, and the broth discarded.

The quiche casserole in the following section, for example, is a main dish that serves 3 to 4 people. It contains only 1/4 cup of meat and does not require sauce.

As always, your diet should be
approved by your physician.

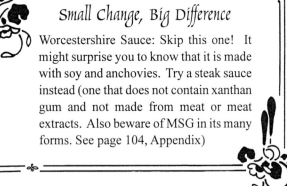

Small Change, Big Difference

Worcestershire Sauce: Skip this one! It might surprise you to know that it is made with soy and anchovies. Try a steak sauce instead (one that does not contain xanthan gum and not made from meat or meat extracts. Also beware of MSG in its many forms. See page 104, Appendix)

Baked Ziti

1 lb. ziti (semolina or semolina durum)
4 tbsp dried chopped parsley
1 tsp dried whole oregano
1/2 tsp garlic powder
1/2 lb part skim ricotta (no xanthan gum)
1/8 tsp pepper
2 1/2 cups spaghetti sauce
1/2 lb. part skim mozzerella, grated

Preparation:

Prepare ziti according to directions on package. Combine cooked ziti together with remaining ingredients. Fold with a large spoon until blended.

Place mixture in a covered baking dish.

Cook in a 450 degree pre-heated oven for 15-20 minutes.

Top with parmesan.

Serves four.

Baked Potato Skins

10 medium potatoes
1/2 lb. reduced fat cheddar cheese, grated
dried oregano, chopped dried parsley, pepper

Preparation:

Wrap potatoes individually in foil. Bake in a 375-degree oven for about 1 to 1 1/2 hours, or until cooked. (Test for tenderness by inserting a fork into the largest potato.) Remove foil and allow to cool for 10 to 15 minutes. Cut potatoes in half. Using a spoon, remove center from potatoes and set aside (leave about 1/4 inch of meat).

Place potato halves, open side up, on a cookie sheet. Sprinkle cheese and spices. Place in oven for about 20 minutes at 375 degrees. Remove and allow to cool.

Makes 20 servings.

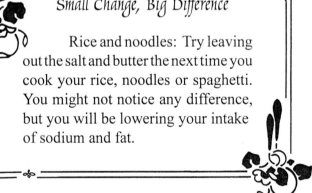

Small Change, Big Difference

Rice and noodles: Try leaving out the salt and butter the next time you cook your rice, noodles or spaghetti. You might not notice any difference, but you will be lowering your intake of sodium and fat.

Caesar Salad

1 bunch of romaine lettuce
1 1/2 cups of white bread, cut into cubes
1/2 cup olive oil
3 fresh cloves of minced garlic
1/2 tsp salt
4 tsp lemon juice
1 egg white
1/2 tsp pepper
1/2 cup parmesan cheese, grated

Preparation:

Set aside 2/3 of the olive oil. In remainder, saute the minced garlic with the cubed white bread until crispy. Remove and place on paper towels to drain. Set aside.

Rinse leaves of the romaine lettuce well under running water. Break, don't cut, into pieces that are bite-sized, and place in large bowl.

Add remaining olive oil. Mix gently with salad forks, distributing oil thoroughly.

Combine lemon juice, egg, salt and pepper. Blend with whisk and mix into salad.

Finally, add parmesan cheese and croutons, mixing one last time.

Serve immediately.

Serves four.

Potatoes au Gratin

3 egg whites
1 cup skim milk
1-1/4 cup grated reduced fat Swiss cheese
1-3/4 lbs. peeled & sliced potatoes (uncooked)
salt, pepper, and nutmeg

Preparation:

This is a special Swiss recipe and can be used as the main dish for your meal. Preheat oven to 350 degrees. Combine milk and eggs, mixing well. Set aside. Place alternating layers of sliced potatoes, cheese and seasonings into a casserole dish that has been lightly coated with canola oil.

Pour the milk and egg mixture gently over the potatoes. Cover and bake for 40 minutes, uncover and continue baking for about 20 more minutes. Allow to cool for 15 minutes. Serves four.

Small Change, Big Difference

Eggs: try using egg whites in place of whole eggs whenever possible. This will help reduce the total amount of cholesterol in your recipe. For example, replace two eggs with three egg whites.

Meat Fried Rice

1/3 cup of chopped boiled meat (turkey or chicken)
1 egg
2 cups of cooked rice
2 Tbsp sesame oil (or margarine)
1/8 tsp garlic powder
salt and pepper

Preparation:

Fried rice is a good dish because, even though there is a good taste of meat, there is a proportionally small amount of meat in the dish itself. Melt oil (or margarine) in skillet. Add meat and saute, stirring, until meat becomes delicately browned.

Add egg, cooking and stirring constantly until egg is fully cooked. Add rice and garlic powder, saute until rice is also delicately browned. Add salt and pepper to taste, remove and serve.

Serves four.

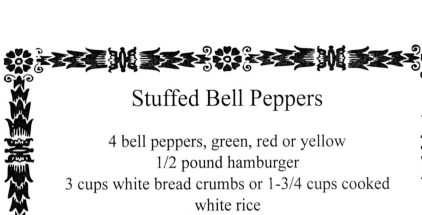

Stuffed Bell Peppers

4 bell peppers, green, red or yellow
1/2 pound hamburger
3 cups white bread crumbs or 1-3/4 cups cooked
white rice
1/2 cup minced onions
2/3 cup spaghetti sauce
1/4 cup warm water
1/4 tsp garlic powder
1 dash salt
1 pinch pepper
1 tsp dried parsley flakes
1/2 tsp dried oregano
3 egg whites

Preparation:

Combine all ingredients (except peppers) in large bowl, kneading by hand until thoroughly mixed and blended. If mixture is too dry to blend thoroughly, add 1/8 cup warm water to help moisten. Remove and discard tops, seeds and pith from peppers.

Fill peppers with stuffing mixture, pressing down into peppers to fill completely. If there is stuffing mixture left over, freeze for using on a later occasion. Place stuffed peppers into covered dish, cooking in preheated oven for about 1 hour at 375 degrees.

Serves four.

Meatloaf

1 small package cornbread stuffing mix
1 pound lean ground hamburger
3 egg whites
One 32 oz. bottle of spaghetti sauce
(no meat, no mushrooms)
1/8 tsp pepper
1/8 tsp salt
1/2 tsp oregano

Preparation:

Lightly coat a 9 x 5 x 3 bread pan with canola oil. Set aside. Prepare stuffing according to directions on package.

Let cool, then combine in large mixing bowl with hamburger, eggs, 2/3 cup sauce, pepper, salt and oregano.

Mix by hand, kneading until a very smooth consistency is reached. Pack mixture into bread pan.

Cover with about 1/4-inch layer of sauce. Lightly sprinkle with a small amount of oregano and pepper.

Cover with aluminum foil. Cook in 350 degree oven for 50 minutes. Uncover and cook for about 25 more minutes, or until sauce on top begins to brown.

Allow to cool and serve in modest slices topped with any remaining spaghetti sauce.

Serves four.

Garlic Chicken with Pasta

1/2 lb. chicken breast, boneless and skinless
12 ounces uncooked pasta
4 cloves minced garlic
1/8 tsp onion powder
1/2 tsp oregano
1 tsp chopped parsley
2/3 cup skim milk
1 tsp flour
1/4 tsp salt
1/8 tsp pepper
1/8 tsp rosemary
2 tsp margarine

Preparation:

Prepare pasta according to directions on package. Drain and rinse. Place in large serving bowl and set aside. While pasta is cooking, prepare chicken as follows: Boil for 10 minutes, discard broth. Chop chicken into small bite-size pieces and set aside. Melt margarine in large skillet. Add chicken to skillet. Cook until chicken is lightly browned. Set aside.

In a separate bowl, mix flour into cold milk with fork until thoroughly combined. Place in large saucepan with garlic, onion powder, oregano, parsley, salt, pepper and rosemary.

Bring to a boil, stirring constantly. Reduce heat and continue to stir until consistency thickens. Combine sauce mixture with chicken and pasta, folding until well combined. Correct seasoning with salt and pepper, if desired. Serves three to four.

Lasagna

1-1/2 cups fat free ricotta or cottage cheese
two 32-oz. bottles spaghetti sauce (no meat or mushrooms)
1 package lasagna noodles
1/2 pound reduced fat mozzarella cheese
1/2 pound reduced fat provolone cheese

Preparation:

Prepare lasagna noodles according to directions on package. Drain, rinse and set aside.

Grate the hard cheeses, combine and set aside.

Lightly coat a deep oven baking dish with olive oil.

Place one layer of lasagna noodles in the bottom of the dish.

Spread an even layer of sauce over the noodles. Over sauce, place a layer of ricotta, mozzarella and provolone cheeses and cover with a generous amount of sauce.

Continue layering ingredients beginning with noodles, etc. until all of the ingredients have been used, ending with a layer of noodles. Cover with a layer of sauce so the top layer will not burn in the oven. Place into a 350 degree oven and bake for about 45 minutes or until sauce on top begins to brown. Can be served hot, but some people say that lasagna tastes better the day after it is cooked!

Serves six.

Quiche Casserole

1 reduced fat baked pie crust
2/3 cup reduced fat Swiss cheese, grated
4 eggs minus 2 yolks
1 small onion, diced
1/2 cup reduced fat cheddar cheese, grated
1 12-oz. can of evaporated skim milk
1/2 bell pepper, diced (optional)
1/8 tsp pepper
1/4 tsp garlic powder
1/4 cup chopped ham

Preparation:

Preheat oven to 375 degrees.

Combine all ingredients (except pie crust) in medium mixing bowl. Stir until mixture is evenly distributed. Pour into pie crust.

Bake for about 55 minutes, or until top of casserole is golden brown.

Serves four to six.

Belgian Waffles

1-3/4 cups white flour
1-1/2 Tbsp sugar
1/2 tsp salt
1/2 tsp vanilla extract
2 tsp baking powder
4 eggs minus 2 yolks
3 Tbsp margarine
1-1/2 cups skim milk

Preparation:

Preheat Belgian waffle iron. Combine flour, sugar, baking powder and salt in bowl. Stir briefly with whisk. Set aside.

In a separate bowl, blend egg whites with electric mixer until quite stiff. Set aside.

Combine milk with melted margarine and egg yolks. Blend with whisk and stir into flour mixture. Consistency will not be smooth.

Gently, but thoroughly, fold in egg whites and vanilla. Be sure to mix completely.

Pour about 2/3 cup of batter into waffle iron. Adjust this amount if necessary. Cook until waffle iron ceases to steam or until waffle becomes golden brown.

Continue to cook waffles until all of remaining batter has been used. Serve with a modest amount of melted margarine and syrup.

Leftover waffles can be refrigerated and re-heated (by microwave or toaster).

Serves four.

French Toast

12 slices white bread
2 eggs minus 1 yolk
1-1/4 cups skim milk
powdered sugar
cinnamon

Preparation:

In a large mixing bowl, combine milk and eggs. Beat with whisk until thoroughly mixed. Heat non-stick skillet on stove at medium high.

Place one slice of bread into egg mixture just long enough to coat outside. Put immediately into skillet.

Coat a second slice and place into skillet. Cook bread on both sides for about 30 seconds each or until coat-ing is well cooked. Some areas may look browned and some merely yellow.

Remove from skillet and place on serving dish. Do not stack.

Coat and cook remaining slices in the same fashion.

Sprinkle powdered sugar and cinnamon onto cooked toast, and serve immediately.

Serves four to six.

Shish Kabob

1/2 pound beef tenderloin
1 bell pepper, green, yellow or red
1 tomato
2 medium potatoes
1 medium onion
lemon pepper seasoning (no MSG)
4 kabob skewers

Boil potatoes in salted water until tender, but not overdone. Cool under running water and peel. Cut into large pieces and set aside.

Wash bell pepper. Remove top, pith and seeds. Cut into 1 1/2-inch squares. Set aside.

Cut onion and tomato into large chunks and set aside. Cut beef loin into small bite-sized pieces, boil for 10 minutes, discarding broth, and set aside.

Place food pieces, one at a time, in patterns onto skewers, leaving 2 to 3 inches at bottom end of skewers and one inch at top.

Arrange skewers neatly on cooking tray and sprinkle generously with lemon pepper. Cook at 350 degrees for about 40 minutes, turning once. Do not allow food to become over-browned. Vegetables should only be cooked enough for flavors to blend. Serve hot.

Serves two.

Chili with Rice

1 small to medium can of turkey chili, no beans
1-1/2 cups of uncooked rice
1 onion, diced
1/4 pound reduced fat monterrey jack cheese, grated

Preparation:

This is a quick dinner that has only a small amount of meat. The meat is further reduced by adding the onions, cheese and rice. In addition, the cheese and rice will also help dilute the overpowering spicy taste that chili can sometimes have.

Prepare rice according to package instructions. While rice is cooking, heat chili in saucepan over medium to high heat, stirring occasionally.

Spoon cooked rice into bowls, filling about half to two-thirds of each bowl. Top with chili, onions and cheese. Serve hot.

Serves four.

Stuffed Tomato Salad

4 large tomatoes
6 eggs minus 2 yolks
4 Tbsp plain nonfat yogurt (no xanthan gum)
1/4 tsp garlic powder
1/8 tsp pepper
paprika
1/2 small onion, minced (optional)
4 large romaine lettuce leaves

Preparation:

Cut off tops and hollow out tomatoes. Set aside. Cook eggs and set aside to cool.

In a medium mixing bowl, combine yogurt, garlic powder and pepper. Blend with wire whisk until smooth. Set aside.

Chop eggs well and add to bowl.

Add onion and mix with spoon until ingredients are well combined. Set aside.

Place lettuce leaves each on individual plates. Place one tomato on each. Spoon egg mixture into tomatoes and top with a small sprinkle of paprika.

With leftover tomato: either set aside for a later date or chop and use as garnish.

Serves four.

Eggplant Parmesan

1 large eggplant
1/2 cup grated parmesan cheese
1/4 cup grated romano cheese
1-1/2 cups reduced fat provolone cheese, grated
4 eggs minus 2 yolks
1-1/2 cups Italian bread crumbs
one 32-oz. jar spaghetti sauce (no mushrooms, no meat)
1 bell pepper

Preparation:

Preheat oven to 350 degrees. Spray a large, shallow (about 1 to 1/2 inches deep) cooking pan with non-stick cooking spray. Remove top and seeds from bell pepper. Cut into bite-sized pieces. Combine with sauce in a medium saucepan and simmer, covered, for about 20 minutes.

While sauce is cooking, pour egg substitute into a medium mixing bowl and set aside. Pour bread crumbs into another bowl and set aside. Remove skin from eggplant. Slice thinly, about 1/4 to 3/8 inch. Set aside.

Pre-heat a large non-stick skillet at medium high heat. One by one, dip eggplant slices first into eggs, then into bread crumbs. Lightly coat with canola oil, then quickly place coated eggplant slice into skillet (do not layer or over-fill pieces in skillet).

Cook on both sides until browned. As each slice is browned, place into the cooking pan. Once all of the slices are in the pan, sprinkle evenly with parmesan, then romano and provolone cheeses. Cover with spaghetti sauce and cook uncovered for about 35 minutes. Serves four to six.

Variations: Once you have tried cooking this dish, it will be easy to make many little variations that can change the flavor each time you prepare it. For example, you can:

-Sprinkle lemon juice and pepper onto the cooked eggplant slices before covering them with the cheese and sauce.

-While preparing the sauce itself, the bell peppers can be omitted, or you can add diced onions, minced garlic, or a variety of vegetables.

-Before baking, the entire dish can be covered with a sprinkling of different spices, such as oregano, parsley, garlic powder, pepper, etc.

These variations are excellent examples of small things you can do yourself to spice up any recipe you prepare in the future. With just a little creativity, you can take a normal recipe and convert it into the favored dish everyone hopes you are going to make again very soon.

Enchiladas

10 flour tortillas
2 cups reduced fat monterrey jack cheese, grated
3/4 cup reduced fat cheddar cheese, grated
1 small onion, chopped
taco sauce, mild or hot
fat-free sour cream (no xanthan gum)
1 large tomato, diced

Preparation:

Preheat oven to 350 degrees. Lightly coat a shallow (about 1 to 1-1/2 inches deep) baking pan with canola oil and set aside.

Place tortillas on dish and cover with plastic wrap. Heat in microwave for about 1 minute, or until softened. Place a 1 1/2" wide layer of monterrey jack cheese through the middle of each tortilla, leaving about one inch on each end. Over the monterrey jack, place a thin line of cheddar, some chopped onion and taco sauce.

Fold over ends and roll tortilla, placing last flap down to keep from unrolling. Place rolled tortillas into cooking pan, cover with aluminum foil and cook for about 30 minutes or until cheese has melted. Remove from oven, uncover, and top with sour cream. Sprinkle with tomato, remaining onion and remaining cheese.

Serves four to six.

Potato Chili

1 small can (8 oz.) tomato paste
1 medium onion, chopped
3 small, or 2 medium, potatoes, peeled
1-1/2 Tbsp dried minced garlic
1 tsp sugar
1/2 packet chili seasoning mix (watch for MSG)
3/4 cup water

Preparation:

Mince potatoes in food processor. Combine with remaining ingredients in medium saucepan. Heat, covered, on medium-high for 15 minutes. Stir frequently. Reduce heat to low and cook for 15 minutes more, stirring frequently. Uncover and cook at medium heat, still stirring frequently, until excess liquid is reduced. Can be served over rice, topped with raw onions and cheese. This dish can also be served as a dip with crackers or chips.

Serves four.

Small Change, Big Difference

If you are planning to serve a dish that contains meat, don't add to the purine level with a meat-based sauce. In addition, beware of sauce mixes which are high in salt and glutamates. Try making your own sauce, such as the Garlic Chicken with Pasta, recipe on page 38.

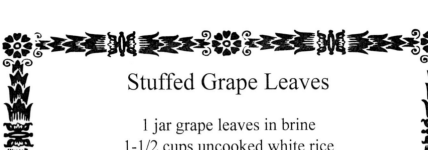

Stuffed Grape Leaves

1 jar grape leaves in brine
1-1/2 cups uncooked white rice
1 zucchini squash
1 yellow squash
3 eggs minus 1 yolk
1/4 tsp pepper
1/4 tsp salt
1 small onion, minced
1/2 tsp garlic powder (or 3 cloves minced garlic)
1/4 tsp whole oregano
two 32-oz. jars of spaghetti sauce
(no mushrooms, no meat)

Preparation:

Remove grape leaves from jar. Unroll, separate and rinse. Remove the stems and tough veins from the bottoms. Set aside.

Cut squash into minced pieces. Place in mixing bowl. Add remaining ingredients, reserving one bottle of sauce. Mix by hand until ingredients are evenly distributed. The grape leaves are now ready for stuffing.

Rolling grape leaves: place a leaf, stem end towards you, in the palm of your hand. Place one heaping teaspoon of the mixture on the stem end of the leaf. Roll once, just until mixture is covered, then fold ends in.

Continue to roll, making sure that the folded ends remain folded. Don't worry if it feels a little loose. Not only will you improve after about 3 rolls, but the rice will swell during cooking and this will make the roll become tighter.

As you complete each roll, tuck snugly into a medium to large sauce pot, loose flap down. Mix the remaining bottle of sauce with 1 quart of water, and pour gently over rolls until the rolls are just covered. Set aside remainder.

Cover. Over medium heat, bring to a gentle boil. Immediately lower heat to simmer and cook, covered, for 1 1/2 hours, or until rice in a top roll is cooked, checking every 15 minutes to see if more sauce mixture needs to be added (Make sure the rolls are always just covered).

Makes about 50 to 60 rolls. Serve hot or cold. This delightful dish can be served either as an appetizer, side or main course.

Manicotti

1 box manicotti shells
2 cups low-fat ricotta cheese
2 egg whites
one 32-oz. bottle spaghetti sauce (no mushrooms, no meat)
4 sprigs fresh parsley, chopped
1/2 tsp whole oregano
grated Parmesan or Romano cheese

Preparation:

Prepare manicotti shells according to directions on box. While shells are cooking, prepare the stuffing: Combine egg with ricotta, parsley and oregano. Mix well until blended. Lightly coat a casserole dish with olive oil.

Spoon ricotta mixture into each shell, filling as well as possible. Place shells into casserole dish, side by side, until all are used.

Cover shells with sauce and bake at 350 degrees for about 45 minutes. Serve with grated parmesan or romano sprinkled generously on top.

Serves four to six.

Sides

- and -

Sauces

Stuffed Tomato Salad II

2 large ripe tomatoes
1 cucumber
3 eggs minus 1 yolk
1/4 cup buttermilk dressing (see page 65)

Preparation:

Cook eggs and set aside to cool.

Wash and remove tops from tomatoes. Discard tops. Hollow out tomatoes with a paring knife, not coming too close to the walls of the tomatoes. Set aside hollowed tomatoes, and place removed portions on a cutting board. Chop, but not too finely.

Pat chopped tomatoes with a towel to remove excess juice. Place in mixing bowl. Peel, quarter and slice cucumber. Add to mixing bowl. Chop eggs and add to mixing bowl. Add dressing and fold until ingredients are evenly distributed. Place mixture into hollowed tomatoes and transfer to serving dishes. Any remaining mixture can be placed decoratively around tomatoes on serving dish and garnished with a small leaf of romaine lettuce. Optional: before serving, the entire stuffed tomato can be cut into quarters with a large knife. Serves two.

Homemade Margarine

3/4 cup butter, softened
3/4 cup canola oil
1/8 tsp salt (optional)

Preparation:
    Combine ingredients in a blender. Blend well until smooth. Transfer mixture to air-tight containers suitable for serving, and refrigerate.
    This is a good alternative for all of the margarines that contain additives.

Don't eat those beans!

Beans are on the list of foods high in purines. Instead of helping yourself to that heaping serving of beans, or even serving beans at all, try preparing another green vegetable instead.

If the idea doesn't sound so hot, try spicing your vegetable up with a nice sauce that can compliment your vegetable (for example, try the dill sauce, page 66 or alfredo, page 76). The more creativity you allow yourself, the more you will look forward to eating.

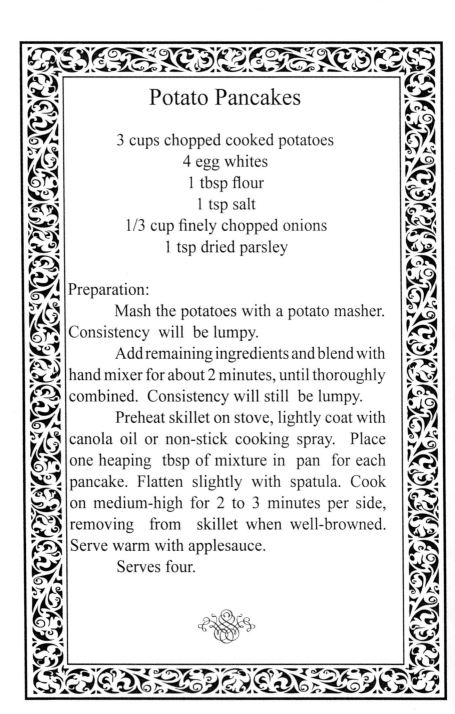

Potato Pancakes

3 cups chopped cooked potatoes
4 egg whites
1 tbsp flour
1 tsp salt
1/3 cup finely chopped onions
1 tsp dried parsley

Preparation:

Mash the potatoes with a potato masher. Consistency will be lumpy.

Add remaining ingredients and blend with hand mixer for about 2 minutes, until thoroughly combined. Consistency will still be lumpy.

Preheat skillet on stove, lightly coat with canola oil or non-stick cooking spray. Place one heaping tbsp of mixture in pan for each pancake. Flatten slightly with spatula. Cook on medium-high for 2 to 3 minutes per side, removing from skillet when well-browned. Serve warm with applesauce.

Serves four.

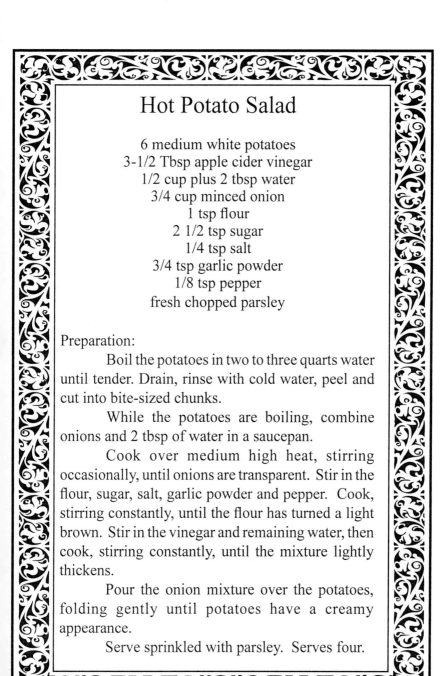

Hot Potato Salad

6 medium white potatoes
3-1/2 Tbsp apple cider vinegar
1/2 cup plus 2 tbsp water
3/4 cup minced onion
1 tsp flour
2 1/2 tsp sugar
1/4 tsp salt
3/4 tsp garlic powder
1/8 tsp pepper
fresh chopped parsley

Preparation:

Boil the potatoes in two to three quarts water until tender. Drain, rinse with cold water, peel and cut into bite-sized chunks.

While the potatoes are boiling, combine onions and 2 tbsp of water in a saucepan.

Cook over medium high heat, stirring occasionally, until onions are transparent. Stir in the flour, sugar, salt, garlic powder and pepper. Cook, stirring constantly, until the flour has turned a light brown. Stir in the vinegar and remaining water, then cook, stirring constantly, until the mixture lightly thickens.

Pour the onion mixture over the potatoes, folding gently until potatoes have a creamy appearance.

Serve sprinkled with parsley. Serves four.

Candied Sweet Potatoes

2 pounds of medium to small
sweet potatoes
1 cup brown sugar, packed
1/3 cup water
1/4 tsp salt
10 large marshmallows

Preparation:

Preheat oven to 400 degrees.

Scrub and rinse potatoes. Submerge in boiling water and cook for about 35 minutes, or until tender (test by piercing center with a fork).

While the potatoes are boiling, combine sugar, water and salt in a sauce pan.

Bring to a boil and continue to boil, stirring, for about 5 minutes.

Remove potatoes from water. Peel and cut lengthwise into halves, then dip into the sugar mixture. Place in a shallow baking pan (lightly coated with canola oil), then pour the remaining sugar mixture over the potatoes.

Cut the marshmallows into quarters and evenly distribute over and between potatoes. Bake at 400 degrees for about 20 minutes, occasionally basting. Serves four.

Baked Butternut Squash

3 butternut squash
2 large sweet onions, minced
1 cup hot water

Preparation:
Preheat oven to 400 degrees.
Line a shallow cooking pan with aluminum foil. Cut squash into halves and remove seeds. Place squash halves in pan, cut side up. Fill evenly with onions. Pour hot water generously into onion filling, gently, until water level reaches top edge of squash.
Place pan into oven and cook about 1 1/4 hours, or until squash is tender when pierced with a fork. While cooking, check on dryness of onions and stir every 30 minutes. Baste squash if needed.
Makes six servings.

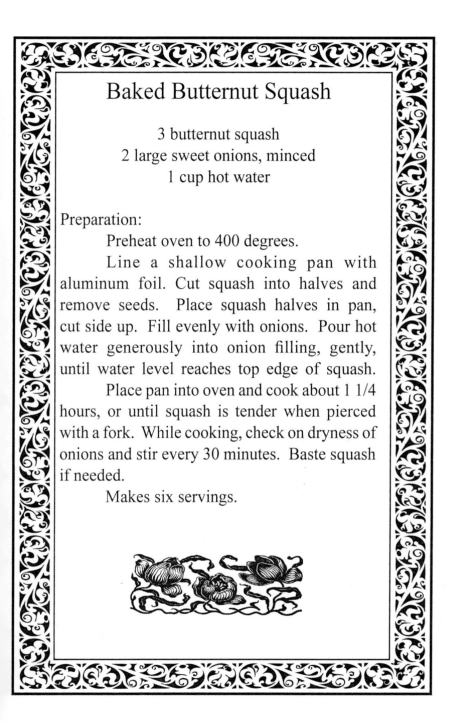

Bleu Cheese Salad Dressing

1 cup fat-free plain yogurt (no xanthan gum)
2 oz. fat-free cream cheese (no xanthan gum)
1 Tbsp lemon juice
4 oz. package of bleu cheese

Preparation:

Blend cream cheese, with an electric mixer in a medium mixing bowl, until smooth.

Drain excess liquid (discarding liquid) from yogurt. Add yogurt and lemon juice to cream cheese. Mix again until thoroughly blended.

Crumble in bleu cheese, fold until evenly distributed and serve.

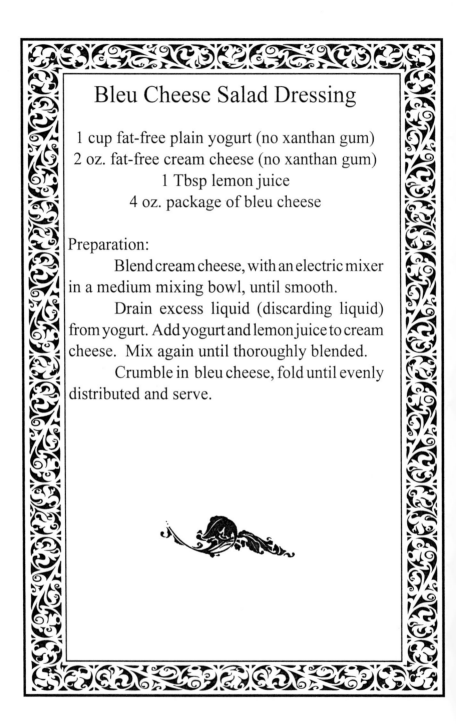

Fried Plantains

2 very ripe plantains, thinly sliced
1/4 cup honey
2 tablespoons margarine

Preparation:

Melt margarine in non-stick saucepan over medium-high heat. Add plantains and honey.

Gently fold, stirring until plantains are evenly coated.

Continue to cook and stir, gently, for about fifteen minutes or until delicately browned and liquid is reduced. Do not burn.

This can be served either as a dessert or a side dish.

Serves four.

Small Change, Big Difference

Chicken noodle soup? Oops! Don't forget, this a soup with meat, made from meat, and relatively high in purines. Try a nice french onion or potato soup instead.

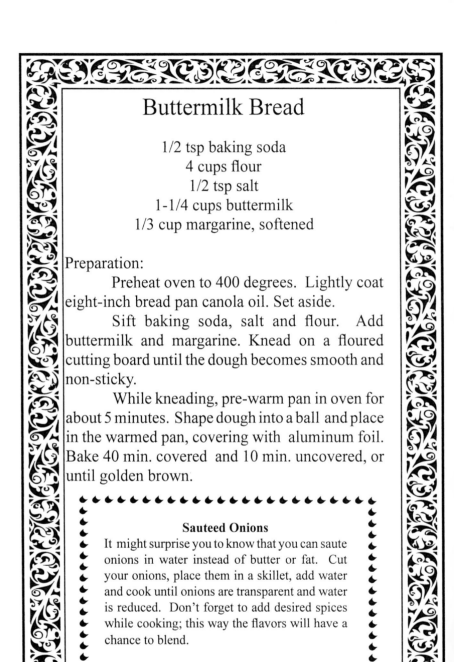

Buttermilk Bread

1/2 tsp baking soda
4 cups flour
1/2 tsp salt
1-1/4 cups buttermilk
1/3 cup margarine, softened

Preparation:

Preheat oven to 400 degrees. Lightly coat eight-inch bread pan canola oil. Set aside.

Sift baking soda, salt and flour. Add buttermilk and margarine. Knead on a floured cutting board until the dough becomes smooth and non-sticky.

While kneading, pre-warm pan in oven for about 5 minutes. Shape dough into a ball and place in the warmed pan, covering with aluminum foil. Bake 40 min. covered and 10 min. uncovered, or until golden brown.

Sauteed Onions

It might surprise you to know that you can saute onions in water instead of butter or fat. Cut your onions, place them in a skillet, add water and cook until onions are transparent and water is reduced. Don't forget to add desired spices while cooking; this way the flavors will have a chance to blend.

Greek Salad

2 cloves garlic
1/2 cup feta cheese, chunks or crumbled
1 tomato, cut into small wedges
1/2 cucumber, cut into slices then halved
1 small onion, thinly sliced into rings
5 or 6 sprigs chopped parsley
1/3 cup pitted black olives
1/3 cup pitted green olives
1 small green, red or yellow bell pepper
1-1/2 Tbsp apple cider vinegar
1/4 cup olive oil
1/4 tsp oregano
2 cups of romaine lettuce, washed and broken
into bite-sized pieces
1 cup red leaf lettuce, washed and broken into
bite-sized pieces
1/8 tsp pepper

Preparation:

This dish should be prepared just before serving, and can also be used as your main dish. When using as a main dish, double recipe. Mince one clove of garlic and set aside. With other clove, rub sides of a large salad bowl. Halve and slice cucumber, and cut tomato into small wedges. Place into bowl. Remove top and seeds of bell pepper. Slice finely and add to bowl. Add cheese, onion, parsley, olives and lettuce to bowl. Set aside.

In a small bowl, combine minced garlic, vinegar, olive oil, oregano, pepper and a pinch of salt.

Mix until ingredients are well combined, and add to salad mixture, tossing gently. Serve immediately.

Serves four.

Polenta

1 cup corn meal
4 cups water

Preparation:

Combine cornmeal and water in sauce pan. Bring to a boil over high heat.

Cover, reduce heat and simmer for about 15 minutes, stirring occasionally, until mixture reaches a thick consistency.

Serve hot.

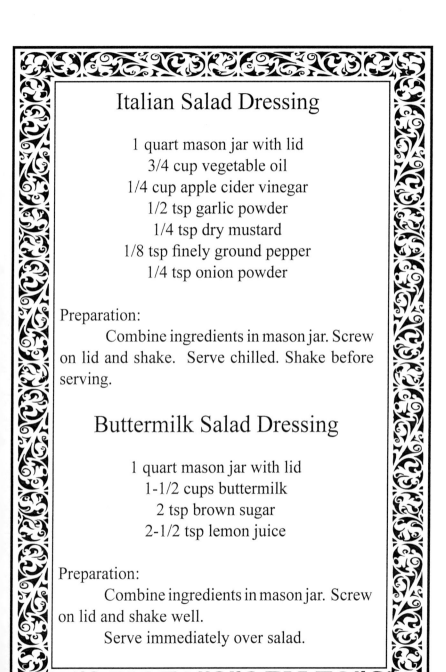

Italian Salad Dressing

1 quart mason jar with lid
3/4 cup vegetable oil
1/4 cup apple cider vinegar
1/2 tsp garlic powder
1/4 tsp dry mustard
1/8 tsp finely ground pepper
1/4 tsp onion powder

Preparation:
    Combine ingredients in mason jar. Screw on lid and shake. Serve chilled. Shake before serving.

Buttermilk Salad Dressing

1 quart mason jar with lid
1-1/2 cups buttermilk
2 tsp brown sugar
2-1/2 tsp lemon juice

Preparation:
    Combine ingredients in mason jar. Screw on lid and shake well.
    Serve immediately over salad.

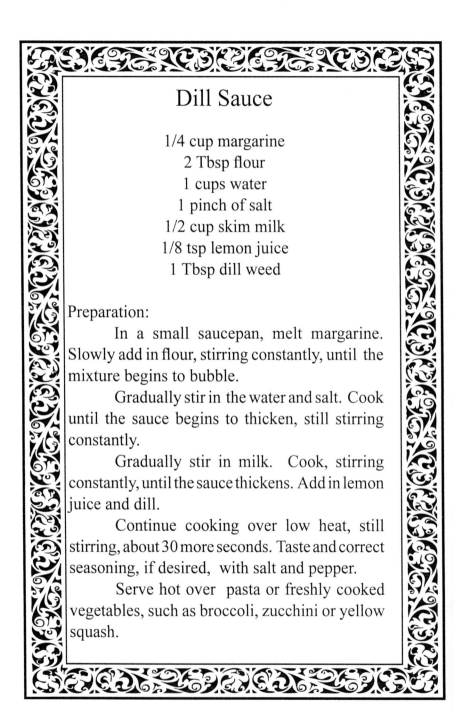

Dill Sauce

1/4 cup margarine
2 Tbsp flour
1 cups water
1 pinch of salt
1/2 cup skim milk
1/8 tsp lemon juice
1 Tbsp dill weed

Preparation:

In a small saucepan, melt margarine. Slowly add in flour, stirring constantly, until the mixture begins to bubble.

Gradually stir in the water and salt. Cook until the sauce begins to thicken, still stirring constantly.

Gradually stir in milk. Cook, stirring constantly, until the sauce thickens. Add in lemon juice and dill.

Continue cooking over low heat, still stirring, about 30 more seconds. Taste and correct seasoning, if desired, with salt and pepper.

Serve hot over pasta or freshly cooked vegetables, such as broccoli, zucchini or yellow squash.

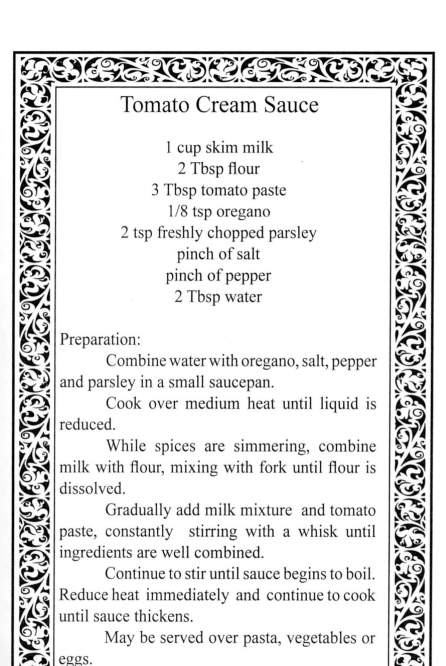

Tomato Cream Sauce

1 cup skim milk
2 Tbsp flour
3 Tbsp tomato paste
1/8 tsp oregano
2 tsp freshly chopped parsley
pinch of salt
pinch of pepper
2 Tbsp water

Preparation:

Combine water with oregano, salt, pepper and parsley in a small saucepan.

Cook over medium heat until liquid is reduced.

While spices are simmering, combine milk with flour, mixing with fork until flour is dissolved.

Gradually add milk mixture and tomato paste, constantly stirring with a whisk until ingredients are well combined.

Continue to stir until sauce begins to boil. Reduce heat immediately and continue to cook until sauce thickens.

May be served over pasta, vegetables or eggs.

Potato Salad

6 medium potatoes
1 cup fat-free plain yogurt
1 small to medium onion, diced
1/8 tsp salt
1/8 tsp pepper
1/4 tsp onion powder
1/4 tsp garlic powder

Preparation:

Boil potatoes until just tender. Chill, remove the skins, if desired, and cut into bite-sized pieces. Place in large bowl. Set aside.

Drain and discard excess liquid from yogurt. Add diced onions, onion powder, garlic powder, salt and pepper to yogurt, blending well.

Add yogurt mixture to potatoes, gently folding until potatoes are evenly coated.

Serves four to six.

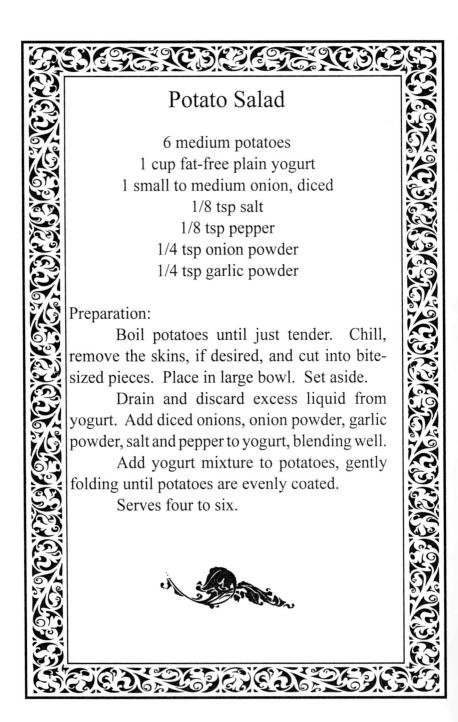

Corn Pudding

6 raw ears of corn, husks removed
2 eggs minus 1 yolk
2/3 cup skim milk
1 tsp sugar
2 Tbsp margarine, softened
1/2 tsp salt
1/8 tsp pepper

Preparation:

Lightly coat a small square baking dish (1 or 2 quart) with canola oil. Preheat oven to 325 degrees.

With the rind-grater portion of a cheese grater, scrape off the tops of the corn kernels, and then scrape with a knife to remove the inner pulp. Place kernels and pulp in a mixing bowl and set aside. There should be approximately 2 cups of pulp.

With a wire whisk, briefly beat the eggs and then add them to the corn pulp.

Add the milk, sugar, margarine, salt and pepper, blending well. Place mixture in baking dish and cook, uncovered, for about one hour.

Serves four.

Pasta Salad

16 ounces of pasta twists
1/2 cup Italian dressing (page 65)
1/4 cup onions, minced
1 Tbsp nonfat plain yogurt (no xanthan gum)
1/4 cup chopped green olives (w/pimiento)

Preparation:

Cook pasta according to directions on package. Drain and rinse with cold water and place in bowl. Add remainder of ingredients, tossing gently until evenly distributed. Chill until ready to serve. Serves four.

Honey Mustard Dressing

2 Tbsp mustard
2 Tbsp vinegar
4 Tbsp oil
1 tsp honey
1/4 tsp garlic
2 shakes of pepper

Preparation:

Combine ingredients in small mixing bowl. Blend with fork until thorough hly combined. Let mixture sit for about 15-20 minutes to allow mustard to absorb ingredients. Blend again with fork and toss into salad or serve as a dip

Baked Broccoli

3/4 cup skim milk
1 Tbsp flour
1/2 cup grated low-fat cheddar cheese
2 bunches of fresh broccoli, chopped

Preparation:
Combine milk and flour in saucepan. Stir well until blended. Cook, stirring constantly, until thickened. Add cheese and stir until melted. Add broccoli and gently fold until evenly distributed. Transfer to baking dish. Bake uncovered in 350 degree oven for 40 minutes. Serves four.

Homemade Applesauce

10 apples
1/2 cup brown sugar, packed
1/8 tsp cinnamon
1/8 tsp ground cloves
1/8 tsp nutmeg
1/8 tsp allspice
1-1/2 cups water
1/2 tsp lemon juice

Peel and core apples. Pulse in food processor. Place in saucepan. Add remaining ingredients. Bring mixture to a boil, then reduce heat, stirring occasionally, and cook until water is reduced. May be served hot or chilled. Serves four to six.

Garlic Potatoes

4 medium potatoes
5 cloves garlic, thinly sliced
1 medium onion, chopped
1 cup water

Preparation:

Boil potatoes until tender. Do not overcook. Cool under running water. Peel and cut into pieces and set aside. In large skillet, saute garlic and onion in 1/2 cup water until onions are transparent. Add more water if necessary.

Add potatoes and remaining water. Continue to saute, stirring gently, until water is reduced and flavor has been absorbed by potatoes. Serve hot.

Serves four to six.

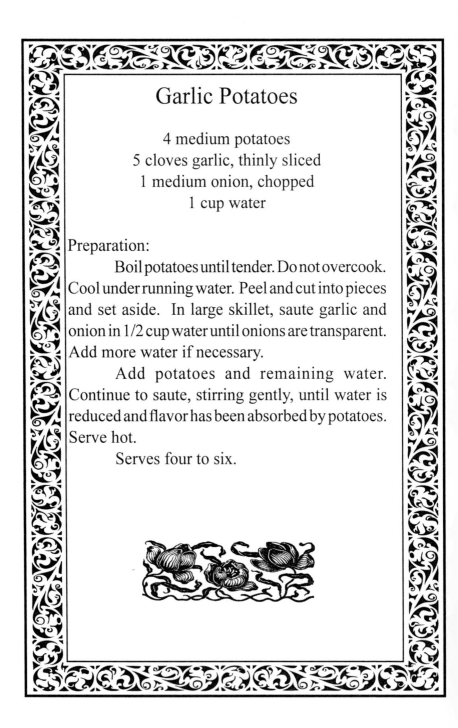

Cucumber Salad

4 cucumbers
1/4 tsp onion powder
1/8 tsp pepper
1/4 tsp garlic powder
2 Tbsp vinegar
5 Tbsp olive oil

Preparation:

Wash cucumbers well. Slice thinly (preferably though the slicer in your cheese grater), discarding end slices that do not have seeds in the center. Place in large mixing bowl.

Add remainder of ingredients and mix well, but gently, with large spoon until spices and liquid are all evenly distributed.

Set aside for about 10 minutes to allow the flavors to soak into the cucumbers.

Taste and correct the seasoning with salt or pepper. Chill for about 1 hour, if desired. Serves four.

Squash and Onions

2 yellow squash
3 small zucchini squash
1/2 small onion
1 cup water

Preparation:

Slice squash and place into large saucepan. Chop onion and add to squash. Add water.

Cook covered over medium high heat until squash becomes tender, stirring occasionally and adding more water if necessary. Uncover and continue to cook, stirring occasionally, until water is reduced.

Serves four.

Small Change, Big Difference

Garlic: Garlic powder and minced garlic can be used instead of salt in many cases. Try spicing up your dinner with a little garlic instead of salt. Your meal will be tastier and healthier.

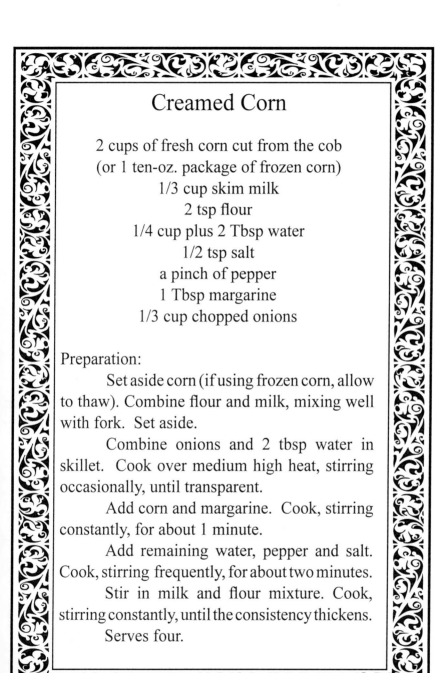

Creamed Corn

2 cups of fresh corn cut from the cob
(or 1 ten-oz. package of frozen corn)
1/3 cup skim milk
2 tsp flour
1/4 cup plus 2 Tbsp water
1/2 tsp salt
a pinch of pepper
1 Tbsp margarine
1/3 cup chopped onions

Preparation:

Set aside corn (if using frozen corn, allow to thaw). Combine flour and milk, mixing well with fork. Set aside.

Combine onions and 2 tbsp water in skillet. Cook over medium high heat, stirring occasionally, until transparent.

Add corn and margarine. Cook, stirring constantly, for about 1 minute.

Add remaining water, pepper and salt. Cook, stirring frequently, for about two minutes.

Stir in milk and flour mixture. Cook, stirring constantly, until the consistency thickens. Serves four.

Alfredo Sauce

2 cups milk
2 tsp cornstarch
3 cloves garlic
1/2 tsp onion powder
1 tsp parsley flakes
1/2 tsp oregano
2 sprinkles pepper
1/2 tsp salt

Preparation:

Combine milk and cornstarch in a mixing bowl. Stir with a fork until the cornstarch is dissolved.

Pour into a sauce pan. Add remaining ingredients. Bring to a boil, stirring constantly.

Reduce heat and simmer, stirring constantly, for about 2 minutes, until sauce thickens.

Serve over pasta or vegetables.

French Dressing

1/4 cup apple cider vinegar
2 tsp sugar
2 Tbsp tomato paste
1/2 cup canola oil
1/2 tsp garlic powder
1/8 tsp pepper
1/2 tsp paprika

Preparation:
Combine vinegar and sugar in a cruet. Cover and shake until sugar is dissolved (20-30 seconds).

Add remaining ingredients, shaking until ingredients are thoroughly combined. Serve chilled, shaking well before serving.

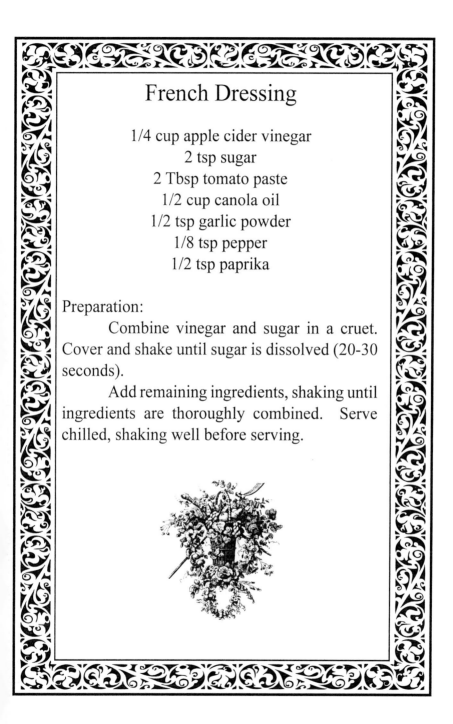

Desserts

Cooked Apples

2 apples
1/3 cup water
2 1/2 tbsp sugar
1 tsp fresh ginger, finely grated
1/2 lemon juice
1/2 tsp vanilla extract

Preparation:

Peel, core and finely slice apples. Set aside.

Combine water and sugar, stirring until sugar is dissolved. Place into medium non-stick saucepan. Add remaining ingredients, including apple slices.

Cooking over medium high heat, stirring occasionally, for about 10 minutes or until apples have softened.

Continue cooking until liquid is reduced and apples are slightly browned. Serve warm.

Serves two to four.

Strawberry Frozen Yogurt Parfait

16 oz. frozen strawberries in sugar
1 cup plain nonfat yogurt
1/2 cup skim milk
2 tsp lemon juice

Preparations

Remove 8 slices of strawberries and set aside for garnish.

Puree remainder of strawberries in blender. Place 1 cup of pureed strawberries in mixing bowl and set aside remainder.

Add yogurt, milk and lemon juice to mixing bowl.

Stir until well blended.

Freeze in ice cream freezer for about 35 minutes or until desired consistency is reached.

Pour a small amount of pureed strawberries into parfait glasses (champagne or wine glasses will work), just enough to cover bottom of each glass.

Spoon in a layer of frozen yogurt, top with remaining pureed strawberries and garnish with strawberry slices.

Serves four.

Almond Crisps

1/2 cup margarine
1 cup sugar
2 egg whites
1-1/2 cups rice flour
1 tsp baking powder
1 tsp almond extract
2/3 cup finely chopped almonds

Preparation:

Lightly coat a cookie sheet with canola oil. Preheat oven to 375 degrees.

Set aside 1/3 cup of almonds. Combine remaining ingredients in medium mixing bowl.

Blend with an electric hand mixer on high for about 3 minutes or until batter reaches a thick fluffy texture.

Spoon batter by teaspoonfuls onto cookie sheet. Sprinkle with remaining almonds.

Bake at 375 degrees for 15 minutes or until browned on edges. Remove from oven.

Cool completely before serving to prevent breakage.

Small Change, Big Difference

Ingredients: Always check labels for ingredients! If a product contains MSG, soy, xanthine or xanthan gum, avoid it. Soy oil is acceptable.

Deluxe Fruit Crepes

1/2 cup flour
3/4 cup skim milk
1 egg
1-1/2 cups frozen berries in light syrup
6-oz. container of low-fat yogurt with berries

Preparation:

Crepes: In a medium bowl, combine flour, milk and egg. Blend with an electric mixer until smooth.

Preheat a medium to large non-stick skillet on medium high for about 30 seconds. Lightly spray a layer of non-stick cooking spray onto the heated surface.

Quickly place 2-1/2 tbsp of batter into pan. Lift the skillet and tilt, rotating the angle of the tilt until the bottom surface of skillet is covered with the batter.

Cook for about 30 to 60 seconds; the bottom surface of the crepe will become lightly browned and the exposed surface, although moist, will lose its wet-batter look.

Do not turn crepe over. To remove from skillet, turn skillet upside down onto serving dish and allow crepe to fall out on its own. Proceed until batter is gone. End result should yield 6 to 8 crepes.

Set aside.

Filling: drain 1/2 of the liquid from the berries. Discard the drained liquid. Set aside 6 to 8 berries for garnish.

Combine berries with yogurt in a medium mixing bowl. Fold gently until liquid is well blended.

Spoon a portion of filling towards one edge of crepe, then roll and place on serving dish.

Continue with each crepe in this fashion until crepes have all been used.

Spoon any excess filling over rolled crepes and garnish with berries. Makes six to eight crepes.

Variations: You can get creative with the fillings used for your crepes. Any fresh fruit is great: blueberries, strawberries, cherries, raspberries, or a combination. For sauce, add fruit yogurt. This is a delightful, delicate dessert.

Homemade Sweetened Condensed Milk

2-3/4 cups skim milk
2/3 cup sugar

Place ingredients in double boiler. Cook, stirring occassionally, until the amount of liquid has been reduced to 1-1/4 cups (about 1-1/2 hours). Equal to one 14-oz can of sweetened condensed milk.

Rice Pudding

3/4 cup chopped walnuts
1-1/2 cup cooked rice
1 dozen chopped prunes or 3/4 cup raisins
1/2 cup brown sugar, packed
1 egg

Preparation:

Preheat oven at 350 degrees. Lightly coat a 9 x 5 x 3 bread pan with canola oil.

Combine ingredients in mixing bowl. Stir with spoon until evenly distributed. The brown sugar and egg will blend together to form a sort of syrup.

Pack mixture firmly in bread pan. Cook at 350 degrees for 40 minutes. Remove from oven, cool 10 minutes, fluff with fork and serve.

Serves four.

Quick Snack

Yogurt for dessert: Begin with a bowl of nonfat vanilla yogurt. Add fresh fruit and enjoy!

Strawberry Shortcake

3 quarts of fresh strawberries
2/3 cup sugar
2 cups flour
3 teaspoons baking powder
1/2 teaspoon salt
1/2 cup margarine, softened
2 egg whites
1/2 cup skim milk
nonfat vanilla yogurt (no xanthan gum)
6 nice whole strawberries for garnish

Preparation:

Preheat oven to 425 degrees. Lightly coat one 8 x 8 baking pan with canola oil. Combine flour, baking powder and salt in large mixing bowl. Add margarine and blend on low speed with electric mixer until crumbly. Gradually add milk and egg. Blend until mixture is smooth.

Transfer to baking pan. Spread batter evenly, patting with fingers if necessary. Bake at 425 for 30 minutes, or until golden brown. Toothpick inserted in center should come out clean. Remove from oven to cool and set aside.

Rinse berries well. Remove the tops and rinse again. Cut into bite-sized pieces (quarters or eighths, depending on size of berries, should do).

Place in a large mixing bowl and add the sugar. The small amount of water remaining from rinsing the berries will be sufficient for making the syrup.

Gently fold the sugar and strawberries, distributing evenly and allowing sugar to dissolve and make syrup. Let sit for about 20 minutes, and fold again.

Remove cake from baking pan by running knife gently along edge and turning upside down. Cut into six rectangles and place in individual serving bowls.

Place generous portions of the strawberry mixture over each piece of cake. Top with vanilla yogurt and whole strawberries.

Serves six.

About Using Extracts

The next time you are in the grocery store, take a look at the ingredients label on vanilla and other extracts. It might surprise you to find that the alcohol content is extremely high. If you are going to use an extract while preparing your meal or dessert, make sure it is in a recipe which involves cooking, so the alcohol will no longer be present once your dish hits the table.

Vanilla Cake

2-2/3 cups flour
one recipe sweetened condensed milk (page 83)
3 egg whites
1/2 cup margarine
1 tsp baking soda
1 tsp vanilla extract
1/3 cup cherry juice
1 cup of pitted cherries

Preparation:

This is a delicate, delicious cake. If you prefer a different cherry taste, use maraschinos instead.

Preheat oven to 325 degrees. Lightly coat an 8 x 8 inch baking pan with canola oil.

Combine ingredients in a medium mixing bowl. Blend with an electric mixer until smooth.

Transfer to baking dish. Bake for 35 to 45 minutes or until top is golden brown. Toothpick inserted in center should come away clean.

Cooked Pears

4 pears
2/3 cup water
3 tsp sugar
1/4 tsp cinnamon
a pinch of nutmeg
a pinch of allspice

Preparation:

Peel and core pears. Cut into bite-sized pieces. Place in saucepan with remaining ingredients.

Bring to a soft boil, then lower heat. Simmer until pears are tender. Serve alone, or over cake or ice cream. Serves four to six.

New Eating Habits: Fun or Punishment?

Frame of mind, especially in the beginning of a new diet, is extremely important to your success. If you look upon your food restrictions as punishment or limitations, then you will never be happy with your meals.

On the other hand, your new life-style is your opportunity to take control over your body's health. When you see your diet as a challenge in creativity, you and your family can enjoy eating more than ever before.

Blueberry Muffins

3 egg whites
one recipe sweetened condensed milk (page 83)
1/4 tsp salt
1/2 cup margarine, softened
2-1/2 cups white flour
3 tsp baking powder
1-1/4 cup fresh blueberries

Preparation:

Preheat oven to 350 degrees. Lightly coat one muffin pan with canola oil. Set aside. Sift and combine flour with baking powder. Set aside.

In a medium mixing bowl with an electric mixer, combine eggs, milk, salt and margarine, blending well.

Slowly blend in flour, mixing until smooth.

Fold in blueberries.

Place mixture in muffin pan and bake at 350 degrees for 25 minutes. Toothpick inserted in centers should come out clean.

Makes about six muffins.

Wild Cherry Ice

1 cup cherry juice
3/4 cup water
4 tsp lemon juice
1/4 cup sugar

Preparation:

Combine ingredients in mixing bowl. Stir until sugar is dissolved. Freeze in ice cream freezer for about 20 minutes or until ice reaches desired consistency. Blend briefly with whisk before serving. Makes 1 quart.

Nutty Bars

1-1/4 cup chopped nuts (walnuts, pecans, etc.)
1/2 cup chopped dates or raisins
1-1/4 cup rice flour
3 egg whites
1 tsp molasses
2 tsp honey
1/4 cup nonfat vanilla yogurt

Preparation:

Lightly coat a 9 x 5 x 3 bread pan with canola oil. Combine ingredients, mixing thoroughly. Place in pan and cook at 350 degrees for 30 minutes or until toothpick comes out clean. Cool and cut. Makes 6 bars.

Orange Cake

4 tsp fresh grated orange rind
1-1/2 cups flour
2 tsp baking powder
1/2 cup plus 1 Tbsp margarine
one recipe sweetened condensed milk (page 83)
3 egg whites
1/2 cup orange juice
3 Tbsp dry white bread crumbs
1 Tbsp butter, softened
4 Tbsp sugar

Preparation:

Preheat oven to 400 degrees. Lightly coat one 8 x 8 baking pan with canola oil. Set aside.

In a medium mixing bowl, combine 1/2 of the orange rind, flour, baking powder, 1/2 cup margarine and milk.

Blend with an electric mixer until ingredients are evenly distributed. Slowly blend in eggs and orange juice, blending until smooth.

Transfer to baking dish. Set aside.

In a small mixing bowl, combine sugar, bread crumbs, remaining orange rind and remaining margarine. Blend well with a fork, then sprinkle over mixture in baking pan.   Bake at 400 degrees for 30 minutes or until a toothpick inserted in the center comes out clean. Cool and serve.

Sweet Potato Pie

1 reduced fat 9-inch pie crust, unbaked
3 egg whites
3/4 cup sugar
1 tsp ground cinnamon
1/2 tsp salt
1/2 tsp ground ginger
1/4 tsp ground cloves
1/8 tsp nutmeg
1/8 tsp allspice
2 cups of canned sweet potatoes
1 cup skim milk

Preparation:

Preheat oven to 425 degrees. Set aside pie crust.

Combine remaining ingredients in a medium mixing bowl.

Blend with an electric mixer until smooth. Pour into pie crust, and cook at 425 degrees for about 15 minutes.

Reduce the temperature to 350 degrees, and continue baking for about 45 minutes or until a toothpick inserted in the center comes out clean.

Remove pie from oven, cool, then chill in refrigerator overnight, or for at least 4 hours.

Serve with ice cream or nonfat vanilla yogurt.

Gingerbread Cake
with Lemon Sauce

one recipe sweetened condensed milk (page 83)
1/4 tsp salt
2 tsp fresh finely ground ginger
1/2 tsp ground cinnamon
1/2 tsp ground cloves
1 cup canola oil
2 teaspoons baking soda
2-1/2 cups flour
2/3 cup molasses
3 egg whites
lemon sauce (see following recipe)

Preparation:

Preheat oven to 350 degrees. Lightly coat one 13 x 9 inch baking pan with canola oil.

In a medium mixing bowl, combine flour, baking soda, salt, ginger, cinnamon and cloves.

Blend with an electric mixer, slowly stirring in first the eggs, oil and milk, then the molasses, blending well. Set aside.

Transfer to baking pan and bake at 350 degrees for about 45 minutes, or until toothpick inserted in center comes out clean.

Cool for about ten minutes and cut into about 12 rectangles. Serve topped with lemon sauce.

Lemon Sauce

1/4 cup margarine, melted
1/2 cup sugar
2 tbsp flour
1-1/4 cups water
1 tsp grated lemon peel
a pinch of nutmeg
2 tsp lemon juice

Preparation:

Blend sugar, flour and water in a small mixing bowl. Stir with a fork until smooth. Place margarine in a small saucepan.

Add the lemon peel and nutmeg, and bring to a boil over medium heat, stirring constantly.

Boil for about three minutes then remove from heat. Stir in lemon juice and serve over cake.

Fruit Salad

3 nectarines or peaches
3 apples
1 plum
1/2 cup orange juice
1 cup chopped pineapple

Preparation:

Cut nectarines and plum into bite-sized pieces and place in large mixing bowl. Core (peel if desired) and cut apple into bite-sized pieces. Add with pineapple to bowl. Pour orange juice over mixture, and very gently fold until there is a uniform coating of orange juice. The orange juice will not only add flavor, it will help prevent browning. Chill and serve.

Serves four to six.

Don't eat too much of that dessert! Once again, please remember to eat everything only in moderate portions, not in excess, and always consult your physician before making any dietary changes.

Virgin Daiquiri

1 cup fruit (strawberries, cranberries, etc.)
2 cups ice
1/2 cup water or skim milk
3 tsp sugar

Preparation:

Combine water (or milk) and sugar in blender and mix for about 15 seconds. Add ice and fruit. Blend until desired consistency is reached. Serve with fruit garnish.

Serves two.

Canteloupe Fruit Salad

1 canteloupe
1/2 cup watermelon pieces
1/2 cup seedless green or red grapes

Preparation:

Cut canteloupe in half. Remove and discard seeds. Hollow out pulp from each half, placing into mixing bowl. Add remaining ingredients to bowl. Fold gently until evenly distributed. Spoon into canteloupe halves and serve.

Serves two.

Bibliography

The information contained in this book was obtained from the following sources:

Aesoph, Lauri M., *How to Eat Away Arthritis*, Revised and Expanded, 1996 Prentice Hall

Arthritis Foundation, "Gout" brochure, 1999, Arthritis Foundation

Arthritis Foundation, "Diet and your Arthritis," brochure, 1999, Arthritis Foundation

Chang, David J., "Of all the ginned joints....," *Patient Care*, March 15, 1996, v.30, n. 5, p. 182 (3)

Choi, Hyon K, M.D, Dr. P.H.; Atkinson, Karen, M.D., M.P.H.; Karlson, Elizabeth W., M.D.; Willett, Walter, M.D., Dr. P.H.; and Curhan, Gary, M.D., Sc. D.; "Purine-Rich Foods, Dairy and Protein Intake, and the Risk of Gout in Men," The *New England Journal of Medicine*, 350;11, March 11, 2004, pp 1093-1103

Ellman, Michael, H. M.D., "Treating acute gouty arthritis," *The Journal of Muculoskeletal Medicine*, March 1992, pp. 71-74

Emmerson, Bryan T. M.D., Ph. D., "The Management of Gout," *The New England Journal of Medicine*, Volume 334 Number 7, February 1996, pp 445-451

Flieger, Ken, "Getting to know Gout," *FDA Consumer,* March 1995 v29 n2

Forbes Digital Tool:" Cool-Lay off the sheep heart and smelt, or else!," wysiwyg://53/http://www.forbes.com/tool/html/97/sep/0920/side2.htm, June 21, 2000, Forbes.com

Ghadirian, P.; Shatenstein, B.; Verdy, M.; and Hamet, P.; "The influence of dairy products on plasma uric acid in women," *Eur J Epidemiol* 1995;11:275-81

Harness, R. Angus; Elion, Gertrude B.; Zoellner, Nepomuk, *Purine and Pyrimidine Metabolism in Man VII, Part A: Chemotherapy, ATP Depletion and Gout*, 1991, Plenum Press, pp. 3, 139-142, 181, 185-203, 217-221, 227-230, 341-344

Lipetz, Philip, M.D., *The Good Calorie Diet*, 1994, Harper Collins Publishers, pp 188-189

Margen, Sheldon, M.D., *The Wellness Encyclopedia of Food and Nutrition*, 1992, University of CA at Berkeley, Health Letter Associates, pp. 91-94, 348-358

Martinez-Maldonado, Manuel, "How to avoid Kidney Stones," *Saturday Evening Post*, Sept.-Oct. 1995, v.267, n. 5, p. 36(3)

MotherNature.com Health Encyclopedia, Low-Purine Diet, http://www. mothernature.com/ency/Diet/Low-Purine_Diet.asp, 1998, Health Notes, Inc.

National Institute of Arthritis and Musculoskeletal Skin Diseases, "Questions and Answers About Gout," fact sheet

Pennington, Jean A.T., *Bowes & Church's Food Values of Portions Commonly Used,* Edition 17, 1998 Lippincott-Raven, p.391

Porter, Roy and Rousseau, G.S., *Gout, the Patrician Malady*, 1998 Yale University Press

Pritikin, Nathan, *The Pritikin Promise*, 1983, Simon and Schuster, pp. 110-111

Purine Research Society, Bethesda, MD, Web-site: http://www2.dgsys.com/~purine/

Sauber, Colleen M., "Still painful after all these years. (gout)," *Harvard Health Letter*, June 1995, v20, n8, p. 6 (3).

Saunders, Carol S., "Gout: Applying Current Knowledge," *Patient Care*, May 30, 1998, v32 n10 p 125

Steyer, Robert, "Arthritis Sufferers put up a spirited fight against chronic pain," *St. Louis Post-Dispatch*, Feb. 14, 1999

Strange, Carolyn J., "Coping with Arthritis in its many forms," *FDA Consumer*, March 1996, pp. 17-21

Talboth, John H; Yu, Ts'al-Fan, M.D., *Gout and Uric Acid Metabolism*, 1976, Stratton Intercontinental Medical Book Corp.

To find out more about gout, information sources include:

Arthritis Foundation
1330 West Peachtree Street
Atlanta, GA
U.S.A.
(404) 872-7100
(800) 283-7800

NIH Osteoporosis and Related Bone Diseases - National
Resource Center
1232 22nd St., NW
Washington, DC   20037-1292
U.S.A.
PHONE: (202) 223-0344 or (800) 624-BONE
TTY: (202) 446-4315
Fax: (202) 293-2356

Purine Research Society
5424 Beech Ave.
Bethesda, MD   20814-1730
U.S.A.
E-mail: purine@erols.com
Web-site: http://www.purineresearchsociety.org/

APPENDIX
Examples of Legumes
Should Be Used in Moderation
(Relatively high in purines)

adzuki beans
black beans
black-eyed peas (cowpeas, black-eyed beans)
cannellini
chick-peas
cranberry beans (not to be confused with cranberries)
fava beans (broad beans)
flageolets
great northern beans
kidney beans
lentils
lima beans
mung beans
navy beans
pinto beans
red beans
soy beans
split peas
butter beans
garbanzo beans
peas
peanuts
white beans
yam beans

Checking for MSG

Although avoiding MSG is beneficial to your diet, detecting MSG and other glutamates can be difficult. Lists of ingredients may not specify glutamates when they are part of other ingredients, such as hydrolyzed protein, yeast extract and autolyzed yeast. Watch for hydrolyzed vegetable protein, which can also be listed as "flavoring." Labels that should be checked include those found on instant soup mix, sauce mix, salad dressing, stuffing mix and seasonings.